Meet big **L** and little **l**.

Trace each letter with your finger and say its name.

L is for

lamb

L is also for

laugh

leaves

lake

lollipop

3

Ll Story

Look at the cute little lamb!

The lamb likes to leap in leaves...

then laugh and laugh!

The lamb likes to lie by a lake
and sip lemonade.

But does the lamb like lollipops?

NO, NO, NO!
The lamb does NOT like
lollipops the least little bit.